#8

THE CONCORD SERIES
of Music and Books on the Teaching of Music
under the Editorship of
THOMAS WHITNEY SURETTE
and
DR ARCHIBALD T. DAVISON

REG. U. S. PAT. OFF.

No. 1200

THE SECOND
CONCORD
ANTHEM BOOK

FORTY ANTHEMS

for the use of

MIXED VOICE CHOIRS IN PROTESTANT CHURCHES

Compiled and edited by

ARCHIBALD T. DAVISON
AND
HENRY WILDER FOOTE

E. C. SCHIRMER MUSIC CO.
221 COLUMBUS AVENUE, BOSTON, MASS.

PREFACE

The editors believe that the music selected for this volume maintains the high standard of quality which prevails in the first Concord Anthem Book, and the same care has been taken to include pieces of varying difficulty, so that the needs of choirs, both large and small, may be met. There are, on the one hand, a number of three-part anthems designed particularly for choirs deficient in men's voices, and these selections are so arranged that all the men, both tenors and basses, may unite on one part. On the other hand a few anthems, being written for a double-chorus, or in more than four parts, require at least a moderately large choir for adequate presentation.

Every accompaniment has been simply arranged on two staves for the organ. Anthems frequently are published with piano accompaniments which are reductions of an orchestral score, and these accompaniments are often impracticable, not only because they require a technique peculiar to the piano, but also because they frequently extend into ranges which are ineffective on the organ.

Much of the music was written to be sung to words in a language foreign to our people, or for forms of worship unfamiliar in Protestant Churches. In other cases the only accessible English texts were barred from our use by copyrights. It has been necessary, therefore, to arrange new English texts for many of the anthems. Great care has been taken to provide words which shall give fitting utterance to the spirit of the music. Double texts have been supplied in a few cases, so that the anthems shall be available for use both by persons who desire to sing the traditional words associated with the music, and by those who prefer a more modern expression of religious thought. Where the original words were Latin, the Latin title has been given underneath the English title.

The editors have been careful to mark 'abridged' all pieces which have been shortened in order to bring them within service length. Such a case is Dvořák's "An Anthem of Praise", which, incidentally, is not offered for use at regular services of worship, but is intended for festival occasions when the church is celebrating some civic or patriotic event.

The music has, perhaps, been underedited, but only with the idea of leaving choir-masters wide scope for individual interpretation.

It is strongly urged that the unaccompanied pieces be performed without instrumental support. The best traditions of church music require this, and it is hoped that choirs will observe that tradition whenever possible.

ARCHIBALD T. DAVISON

HENRY WILDER FOOTE

INDEX OF COMPOSERS

INDEX OF OCCASIONS

Behold a star from Jacob shining

(From "Christus")

Words arranged by H. W. F.
from Numbers, 24: 17

*Edited, and the Organ part
arranged, by A. T. D.*

Felix Mendelssohn-Bartholdy
(1809-1847)

4

shi - ning,_____ from Ja - - cob_ shi -
shi - ning,_____ from Ja - cob shi - -
shi - - ning, from Ja - cob shi - -
star,___ a star from Ja - cob shi - -

ning,
ning,
ning,
ning,

l.h.
r.h.

Ped.
(senza Ped.)

6

glo - - ry o - ver the na - tions,
glo - - ry o - ver the na - tions,
dim.
glo - - ry o - ver the na - tions, o - ver the
glo - - ry o - ver the na - tions:
dim.
f
to reign in
f
to reign in glo - ry, in
f
na - tions, to reign in glo - ry, in
f
Be - hold a star from Ja - cob shi - ning,
f

8

E. C. S. № 987

12

E.C.S. Nº 987

13

14

some bright morn-ing star is he, The

some bright morn-ing star is he, The

some bright morn-ing star is he, The

some bright morn-ing star is he, The

p

cresc.

prom - ise of the com - ing

cresc.

prom - ise of the com - ing

cresc.

prom - ise of the com - ing

cresc.

prom - ise of the com - ing

cresc.

16

E.C.S. No 987

ing.

ing.

ing.

(senza Ped.)

E.C.S. No 987

To God on high be glory

(Jesu, nun sei gepreiset)

English version by H.W.F.
*Edited, and the Organ part
arranged, by A.T.D.*

Johann Sebastian Bach
(1685-1750)

* It may be found effective to omit all the 'holds' (⌢) in the following $\frac{3}{4}$ section, with the exception of the one which immediately precedes the return to the $\frac{4}{4}$.

men, _____ Our true de - vo - tion voic - ing, Re -

men, _____ Our true de - vo - tion voic - ing, Re -

men, _____ Our true de - vo - tion voic - ing, Re -

men, _____ Our_ true_ de - vo - tion_ voic - ing,_ Re -

Ped.

peat the glad A - men.

peat the glad_ A - men.

peat the_ glad A - men.

peat_ the_ glad A - men.

While by our sleeping flock we lay

(The Song of the Shepherds)
(Unaccompanied)

English version by H.W.F.

Edited by A.T.D.

German Melody: 17th Century
Arranged by Hugo Jüngst

*The expression marks in each verse may be varied as desired. Published also for Women's

**Echo:—To be sung by a small chorus at a distance.

Voices (3-pt.) № 1848.

E.C.S. № 989

Copyright, 1936, by E.C.Schirmer Music Co.
For all countries

Praise ye the Lord on high with joy! Praise ye the Lord on high with joy!

2. Spake then the an-gel, "News I bring Of Is-rael's long-ex-pect-ed king!"

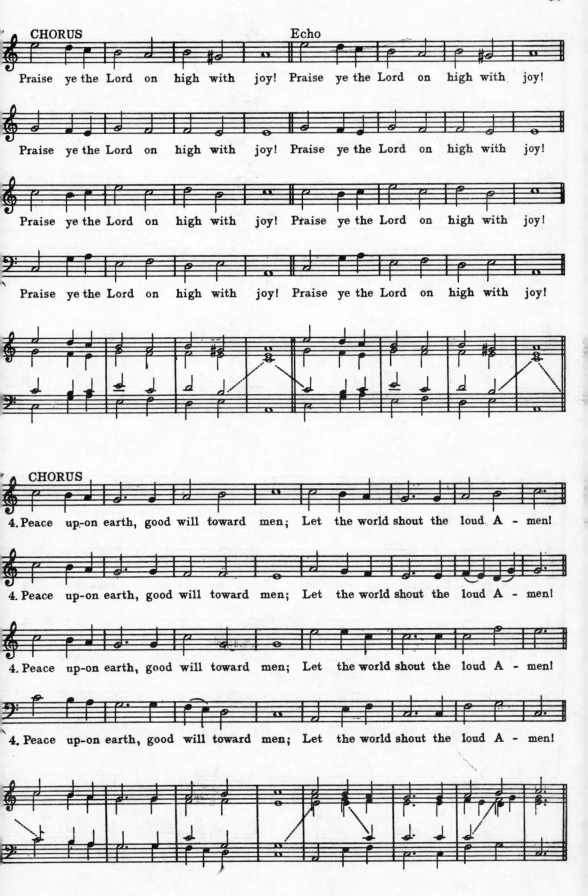

28

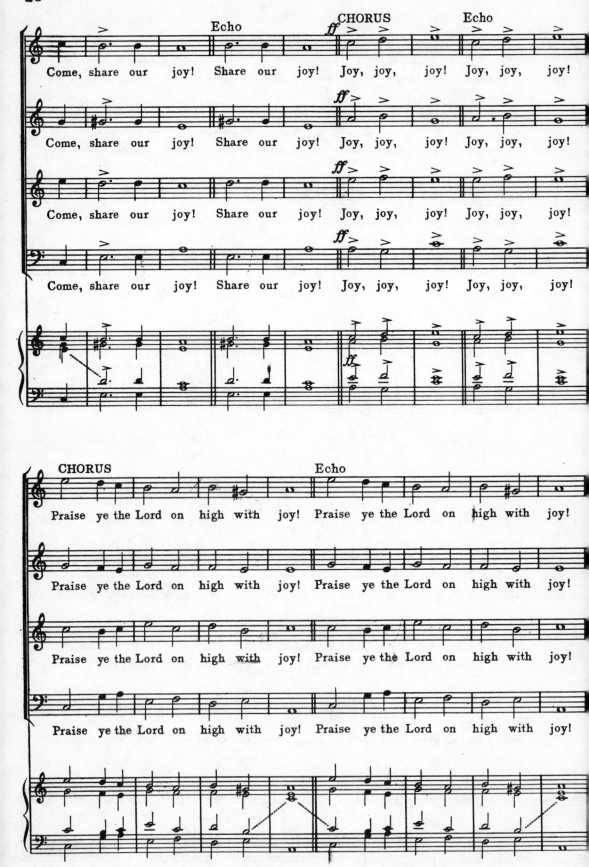

Almighty and everlasting God

(Unaccompanied)

From 'The Book of Common Prayer'

Edited by A.T.D.

Orlando Gibbons
(1583-1625)

E.C.S. Nº 990

30

E. C. S. №990

and in all our dan - gers and ne - ces - si - ties,

ties, and in all our dan - gers and ne - ces -

ties, and in all our dan - gers

ties, and in all our

and in all our dan - gers and ne - ces - si - ties

- si - ties, and in all our dan - gers and ne - ces - si -

and ne - ces - si - ties, our dan - gers and ne - ces - si -

dan - gers and ne - ces - si - ties, our ne - ces - si -

32

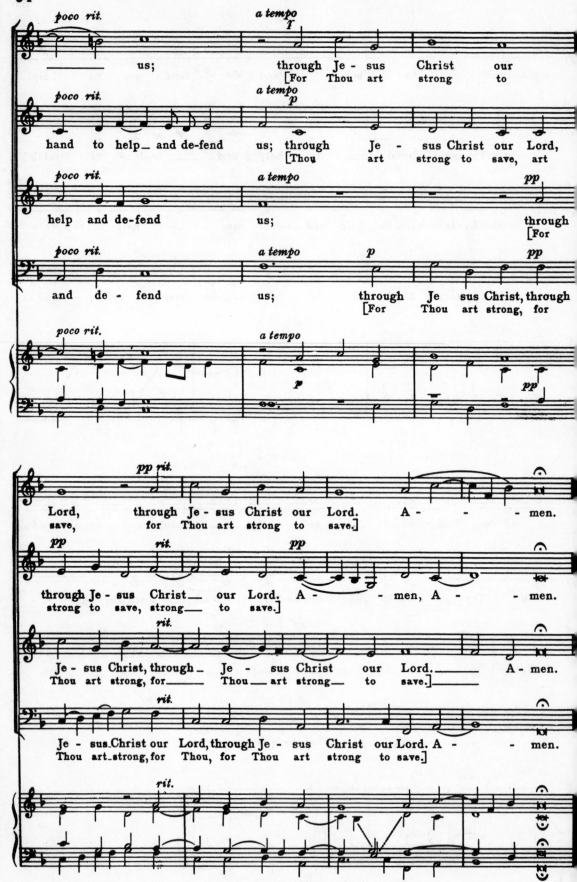

Father, Thy Holy Spirit send

(Jesu, dein Seel')

(Unaccompanied)

Words by H.W.F.
Edited by A.T.D.

Melchior Franck
(1573-1639)

.C.S. Nº 991

36

E.C.S. Nº 991

Lord, to Thee we turn

(Inimici autem)

(Unaccompanied)

Words by H.W.F.

Edited by A.T.D.

Orlando di Lasso
(1532-1594)

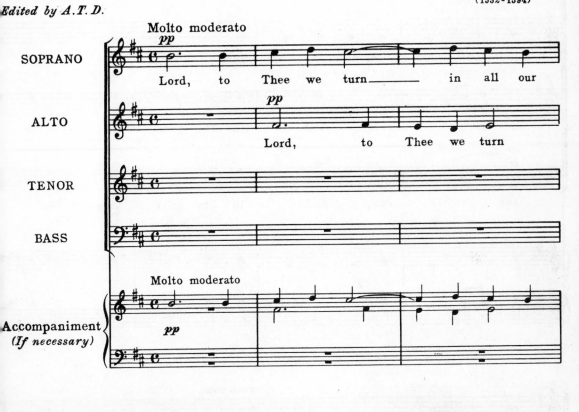

Published also for Men's Voices,— Latin text (E.C.S. Nº954).

E.C.S. Nº992

Copyright, 1936, by E.C.Schirmer Music Co.
For all countries

Remember not, Lord, our offences

[Remember me, Lord, in Thy mercy]

From 'The Book of Common Prayer'
Alternative words adapted
by H.W.F. from
Wisdom of Solomon, 15: 1-3

Edited by A.T.D.

Henry Purcell
(1658-1695)

*The accompaniment should be used only in case instrumental support is necessary.

E.C.S. No 993

41

42

E.C.S. No 993

44

E.C.S. Nº 993

Since Christ his head in sorrow bowed
(From "The Seven Last Words")
(Unaccompanied)

English version by H.W.F.

Edited by A.T.D.

Heinrich Schütz
(1585-1672)

Published also for Men's Voices, (E.C.S. Nº 88)

Copyright, 1936, by E.C.Schirmer Music Co.
For all countries

E.C.S. Nº 994

In pain,_____ in pain_____ be-yond all

_ be-yond all meas - ure, In pain_____ be-yond_____ all

_ be-yond all meas - ure, In pain be - yond all

_ be-yond all meas - ure, In pain, in pain_____ be-yond all

meas - - ure, In pain_____ be-yond all meas -

meas - ure,

meas - ure, *mf* The sev - en words which then he

meas - ure, *mf* The sev - en words which then he

meas - ure, *mf* The sev - en words which then_____ he

- - ure, *mf* The sev - en words which then he

mf

48

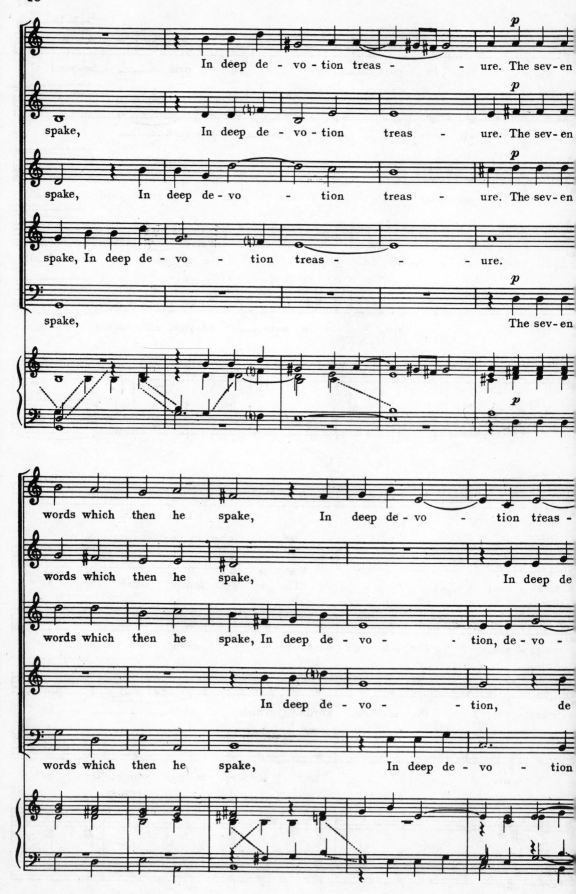

50

Dark was the earth with clouds
(Tenebræ factæ sunt)
(Unaccompanied)

Words adapted by H. W. F.
from the Gospel

Edited by A. T. D.

Johann Michael Hayd
(1787-1806)

SOPRANO

Dark was the earth with clouds, while Je - sus was done to

ALTO

Dark was the earth with clouds, while Je - sus was done to

TENOR

Dark was the earth with clouds, while Je - sus was done to

BASS

Dark was the earth with clouds, while Je - sus was done to

Accompaniment
(If necessary)

death on the cross. It was a - bout the ninth hour; then with a loud

death on the cross. It was a - bout the ninth hour; then with a loud

death on the cross. It was a - bout the ninth hour; then with a loud

death on the cross. It was a - bout the ninth hour; then with a loud

E. C. S. Nº 995

voice he cried out, say-ing, My God, my God! O

voice he cried out, say-ing, My God, my God! O

voice he cried out, say-ing, My God, my God! O

why_ hast Thou_ for-sak-en me? Then he in an-guish

why hast Thou_ for-sak-en me? Then he in an-guish

why hast Thou for-sak-en me? Then he in an-guish

why hast Thou_ for-sak-en me? Then he in an-guish

52

bow'd his head and yield-ed un - - to death.

bow'd his head and yield-ed un - to death.

bow'd his head and yield-ed un - to death.

bow'd his head and yield-ed un - to death.

Larghetto

And once more Je - sus with a loud voice cried out, Fa - ther,

And once more Je - sus with a loud voice cried out, Fa - ther,

And once more Je - sus with a loud voice cried out, Fa - ther,

And once more Je - sus with a loud voice cried out, Fa - ther,

Larghetto

in to Thy hands I com - mend_____ my spir - it. Then a - gain_____

in to Thy hands I com - mend_____ my spir - it. Then a - gain_____

in to Thy hands I com - mend_____ my spir - it. Then a - gain_____

in to Thy hands I com - mend_____ my spir - it. Then a - gain_____

bow - ing down his head, he yield - ed un - to death.

bow - ing down his head, he yield - ed un - to death.

bow - ing down his head, he yield - ed un - to death.

bow - ing down his head, he yield - ed un - to death.

Alleluia! We sing with joy

Words by H.W.F.

*Edited, and the Organ part
arranged, by A.T.D.*

Jacob Hand
(1550-1591)

* If there are not enough singers to make two Choruses, all the singers may be assigned to Chorus
I, the Organ supplying the vocal parts of Chorus II.

Published also for Men's Voices, — Latin text (E. C. S. No 931).

E. C. S. No 996

62

Now God be praised in heav'n above
(Gelobt sei Gott)
(Unaccompanied)

English version by H. W. F.

Edited by A. T. D.

Melchior Vulpi

(1560?-1616)

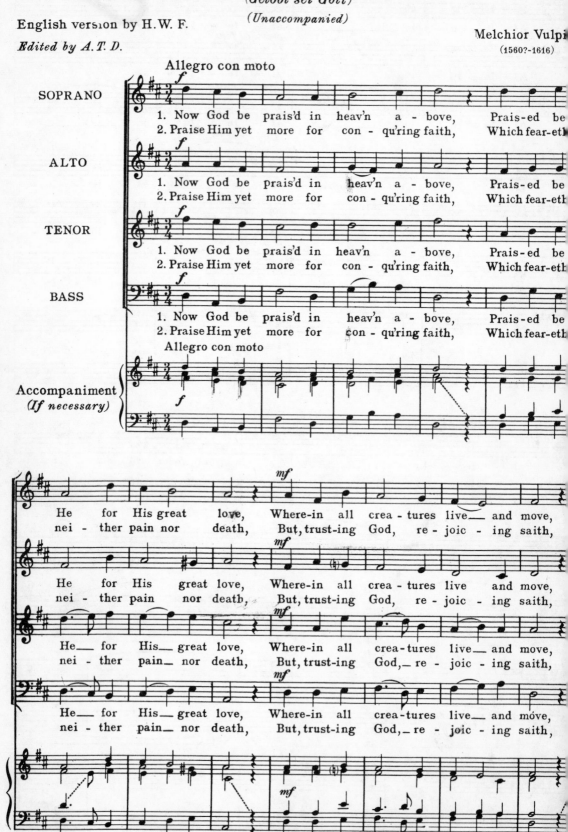

Hal-le-lu - jah,——— hal-le-lu - jah,——— hal-le-lu - jah!

Hal-le - - -lu - jah, hal-le - - -lu - jah, hal-le-lu - jah!

Hal-le-lu - jah,——— hal-le-lu - jah, hal-le-lu - jah!

Hal-le-lu - jah,——— hal-le-lu - jah,——— hal-le-lu - jah!

3. His grace de - fends us from all ill; His Christ shall be our

3. His grace de - fends us from all ill; His Christ shall be our

3. His grace de - fends us from all ill; His Christ shall be— our

3. His grace de - fends us from— all ill; His Christ shall be— our

Adore Almighty God
('Cherubim Song')
(Unaccompanied)

Words by H.W.F.
Edited by A. T. D.

Alexander Tikhonovitch Gretchaninov
(1864-   )

66

more in light a - bove;___ sing, ye morn-ing stars; chant to-

more in light a - bove; sing,___ ye morn-ing stars; chant to-

more in light a - bove;___ sing,___ ye morn-ing stars; chant to-

more in light a - bove;___ sing, ye morn-ing stars;

(Ped

geth-er, ye heav'n-ly hosts, yea, all ye saints at rest, joy to

geth-er, ye heav'n-ly hosts, yea,_ all_ye saints now bless___

geth-er, ye heav'n-ly hosts, bless,___

sing, ye heav'n-ly hosts,

bless— His Name,— for He is Ho - ly, Ho - ly,

His Name,— for He is Ho - ly, Ho - ly,

bless His Name,— for He is Ho - ly, Ho - ly,

bless— His— Name, Ho - ly, One,

(Ped.)

none— is like— to Him for ho - li-ness: chant— now— His

none— is— like— to Him for ho - li-ness: chant—

none— is like to Him— for ho - li-ness: chant—

like— Him a - lone ho - ly:

70

Lord, God the Ho - ly One, shall be praise, __ hon - or and glo - ry ev - er-

Lord, God the Ho - ly One, shall be praise, __ hon- or and glo - ry ev - er-

Lord, God the Ho - ly One, shall be praise, __

Lord, God the Ho - ly One, shall be praise, __

more, from all the host of heav'n. __ Al - le - lu - ia, al - le-

more, from all the host of heav'n. __ Al - le - lu - ia, al - le-

Al - le - lu - ia, al - le-

Al - le - lu - ia, al - le-

71

lu - ia, al - le - lu - ia, al - - le - lu - ia,
lu - ia, al - le - lu - ia, al - - le - lu - ia,
lu - ia, al - le - lu - ia, al - - le - lu - ia,
lu - ia, al - le - lu - ia, al - - le - lu - ia,

al - le - lu - ia, al - - le - lu - i - a!
al - le - lu - ia, al - - le - lu - i - a!
al - le - lu - ia, al - - le - lu - i - a!
al - le - lu - ia, al - - le - lu - i - a!

Mighty Spirit, all transcending
(*Ave verum Corpus*)

Words by H.W.F.

Edited by A.T.D.

Wolfgang Amadeus Mozart
(1756-1791)

73

Pass - ing all— our un- der- stand-ing, In splen - - dor veil'd from

Pass - ing all our un- der- stand-ing, In splen-dor veil'd from

Pass - ing all— our un- der- stand-ing, In splen-dor veil'd from

Pass - ing all— our un- der- stand-ing, In splen-dor veil'd from

mor - tal sight, Hush'd be-

mor - tal sight, Hush'd be-

mor - tal sight, Hush'd be-

mor - tal sight, Hush'd be-

fore_Thee, now_ a - dor - ing, Hearts in si - lent_ hom - ag

fore Thee, now a - dor - ing, Hearts in si - lent hom - ag

fore Thee,_ now a - dor - ing, Hearts in si - lent_ hom - ag

fore_Thee, now a - dor - ing, Hearts in si - lent_ hom - ag

bow'd, Lo, Thy chil - dren_ wait Thy bless-ing, Thy ho -

bow'd, Lo, Thy chil - dren_ wait Thy bless-ing, Thy ho -

bow'd, Lo, Thy chil - dren_ wait Thy bless-ing, Th

bow'd, Lo, Thy chil - dren_ wait Thy bless-ing, Th

Now with hands to God uplifted
(Ecce panis angelorum)
(Unaccompanied)

Words by H.W.F.

Edited by A.T.D.

Antonio Lotti
(1667 - 1740)

Thou all transcendent Deity

(Jesu, Rex admirabilis)

(Unaccompanied)

Words by H.W.F.

Edited by A.T.D.

Giovanni Pierluigi da Palestrin

(1526 - 1594)

Published also for Women's Voices,—3-part (E.C.S. Nº1074).

How excellent Thy Name, O Lord

(abridged)

Psalm 8: 1

*Edited, and the Organ part
arranged, by A.T.D.*

Georg Friedrich Händel
(1685 - 1759)

How ex - cel-

How ex - cel-

How ex - cel-

How ex - cel-

cresc.

Ped.

lent,   how ex - cel - lent Thy Name, O

lent,   how ex - cel - lent Thy Name, O

lent,   how ex - cel - lent Thy Name, O

lent,   how ex - cel - lent Thy Name, O

Lord,   In   all   the

Lord,   In   all   the

Lord,   In   all   the

Lord,   In   all   the

l.h.

world   is known,   in   all   the

world   is   known,   in   all   the

world   is   known,   in   all   the

world   is   known,   in   all   the

l.h.

world is known! How ex - cel - lent,

world is known! How ex - cel - lent,

world is known! How ex - cel - lent,

world is known! How ex - cel - lent,

how ex - cel - lent Thy Name, O

how ex - cel - lent Thy Name, O

how ex - cel - lent Thy Name, O

how ex - cel - lent Thy Name, O

Lord, In all the world is known,

Lord, In all the world is known,

Lord, In all the world is known,

Lord,

in all the world is known! How ex - cel

in all the world is known! How ex - cel

in all the world is known! How ex - cel

in all the world is known! How ex - cel

heav'ns, O King, a - dor'd, How hast Thou set Thy glo-rious

How hast Thou set Thy glo-rious throne, Thy glo - rious

throne, Thy glo - - - - - rious throne,

cresc.

throne, A - bove all heav'ns, O King, a - dor'd,_____ O

mf

A - bove all heav'ns, O King, a - dor'd, O King,

mf cresc.

A - bove all

mf cresc. poco a poco

senza Ped.

88

Hallelujah!

Edited, and the Organ part arranged, by A.T.D.

Georg Friedrich Händel
(1685-1759)

senza Ped.

hal - le - lu - jah, hal - le - lu - jah,_____ hal - le - lu -

hal - le - lu - jah, hal - le - lu - jah, hal - le - lu -

hal - le - lu - jah, hal - le - lu - jah, hal - le - lu -

hal - le - lu - jah, hal - le - lu - jah,

ff

jah, hal - le - lu - jah, hal - le - lu - jah,_____

ff

jah, hal - le - lu - jah, hal -

ff

jah, hal - le - lu - jah,_____

ff

hal - le - lu - jah,

hal-le-lu - jah,_____ hal-le-lu- jah, hal-le - lu-

le - lu - jah,_____ hal-le-lu-

hal-le-lu - jah, hal-le - lu-jah,_____ hal-le - lu-

hal - le - lu jah,_____ hal-le - lu-

jah, hal - le - lu - jah, hal - le - lu - jah, hal-le - lu-

jah, hal - le - lu - jah, hal - le - lu - jah, hal-le - lu-

jah, hal - le - lu - jah, hal - le - lu - jah, hal-le - lu-

jah, hal - le - lu - jah, hal - le - lu - jah,_____

senza Ped.   Ped.

O give thanks unto the Lord

(abridged)

Psalm 106: 1, 4, 48

Edited, and the Organ part arranged, by A. T. D.

Henry Purcel
(1658–1695)

Copyright, 1936, by E.C. Schirmer Music Co.
For all countries

O give thanks,

O give thanks, give thanks un - to the

O, O, O give thanks, give thanks un - to the

O, O, O give thanks, give thanks un - to the

give thanks un - to the Lord,

mf

Lord, give thanks un - to the Lord, for He is gra - cious, is

mf

Lord, give thanks un - to the Lord, for He is gra - cious, is

mf

Lord, give thanks un - to the Lord, for He is gra - cious,

mf

senza Ped.

98

for He is gra- cious, is gra- cious, is

gra- cious, is gra- cious, for He is gra - - cious, is - cious, is

gra- cious, is gra - cious, for He is gra- cious, is gra- cious, is

is gra - cious, for He is gra- cious, is

Ped.

gra - cious. O give thanks, give

gra - cious. O give thanks, O give thanks, give thanks, give

gra - cious. O give thanks, O give thanks, give thanks, give

gra - cious. O give thanks, O give thanks, give thanks, give

E. C. S. Nº 1004

thanks,   O,

thanks, give   thanks, O,   O,

thanks, give   thanks, O,   O,   O,

thanks, give   thanks,   O,   O,   O,

O,   O give   thanks   un - to   the   Lord,

—   O,   O give   thanks   un - to   the   Lord, give

—   O,   O give   thanks   un - to   the   Lord, give

O,   O give   thanks   un - to   the   Lord, give

senza Ped.

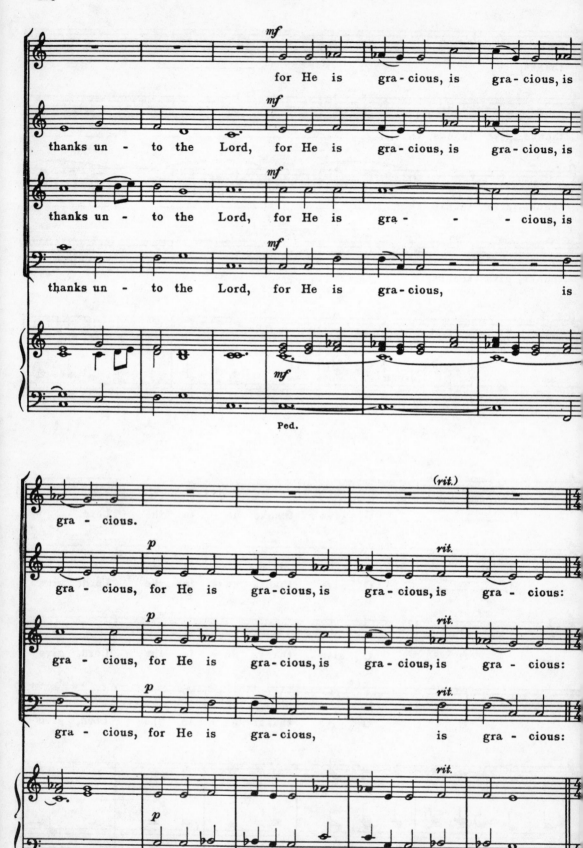

Andante

senza Ped.

ac-

Re-mem-ber, re-

Re-mem-ber, re-mem-ber, re-mem - ber me, O Lord,

ac-cord-ing to the fa-vor that Thou

Ped.

me, O Lord, ac - cord-ing to the fa - vor that Thou

peo - ple, re - mem - ber, re - mem - ber, re -

bear'st un - to Thy peo - ple, ac -

Lord, ac - cord-ing to the fa - vor that Thou bear'st un - to Thy

bear'st un - to Thy peo - ple, re - mem - ber me, O

mem - ber me, O Lord, re - mem - ber me, O

cord - ing to the fa - vor that Thou bear'st un - to Thy

peo - ple, re -

senza Ped.

vis-it me with Thy__ sal-va-tion, O vis-it me, O

O vis-it me with Thy sal-va-tion, O vis-it me,

O vis-it me with Thy__ sal-va-tion, O vis-it me,

vis-it me with Thy sal-va-tion, O vis-it me, O

(senza Ped.)

vis-it me, O vis-it me with Thy__ sal-va-tion,

O vis-it me, O vis-it me with Thy sal-va-tion,

O vis-it me, O vis-it me with Thy__ sal-va-tion,

vis-it me, O vis-it me with Thy sal-va-tion,

Bless-ed, bless-ed be the Lord God E-ter-nal,

Bless-ed, bless-ed be the Lord God E-ter-nal, from ev-er-

Bless-ed, bless-ed be the Lord God E-ter-nal, from ev-er-

Bless-ed, bless-ed be the Lord God E-ter-nal,

Bless-ed, bless-ed be the

last - - - ing, ev-er-last-ing, Bless-ed, bless-ed be the

last - - - ing, ev-er-last-ing, Bless-ed, bless-ed be the

Bless-ed, bless-ed be the

(senza Ped.)   Ped.

out end, and world with-out end, and world with - out_____ end:

world with-out end, and world with-out end, world with - out end

end, and world with-out end, world_____ with-out end:

end, and world with-out end, with - out_____ end:

and let all the peo-ple say, let all the peo-ple say, A-men, A-

and let all the peo-ple say, let all the peo-ple say, A-men, A-

and let all the peo-ple say, let all the peo-ple say, A-men, A-

and let all the peo-ple say, let all the peo-ple say, A-men, A-

senza Ped.

Ped.

An Anthem of Praise

(Praise Jehovah: Psalm 149)
(abridged)

Words by H. W. F.
Edited, and the Organ part
arranged, by A.T.D.

Antonın Dvoř
(1841–1904)

113

.C.S. No 1005

114

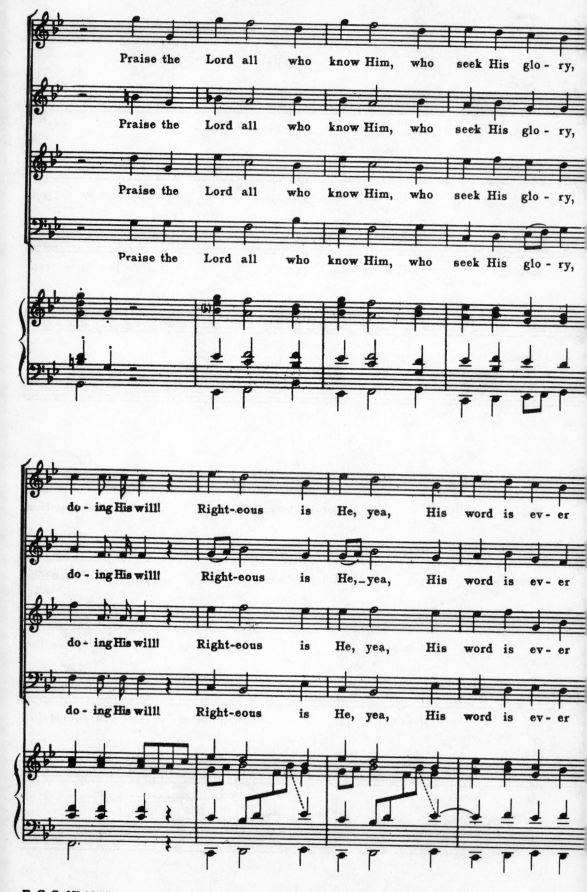

116

last - ing and true!   Hal - le - lu - jah!

last - ing and true!   Hal - le - lu - jah!

last - ing and true!   Hal - le - lu - jah!

last - ing and true!   Hal - le - lu - jah!

Hon-or!   Glo-ry!

Hon-or!   Glo-ry!   Hal -

Hon-or!   Glo-ry!   Hal -

Hon-or!   Glo-ry!   Hal -

Ped.

Hal-le - lu-jah, — hal-le - lu-jah, — hal-le - lu - jah,

le - lu - jah, hal-le - lu - jah, hal-le - lu - jah, hal - le

- le - lu - jah, hal-le - lu - jah, hal-le - lu - jah!

- le - lu - jah, hal-le - lu - jah, hal-le - lu - jah, hal - le - lu

hal - le - lu - jah, — hal - le - lu - jah! Sing hal-le

- lu - jah, hal-le - lu - jah, — ha - le - lu - jah, — hal-le

Hal-le - lu - jah, — hal - le - lu - jah, hal-le

- jah, hal-le - lu - jah! Sing hal-le

120

ty, through - out all a - ges, Who doth gov - ern

ty, through - out all a - ges, Who doth gov - ern

ty, through - out all a - ges, Who doth gov - ern

ty, through - out all a - ges, Who doth gov - ern

all in earth and Heav - - en. For His king-dom

all in earth and Heav - - en. For His king-dom

all in earth and Heav - - en. For His king-dom

all in earth and Heav - - en. For His king-dom

shall be known, His will be done, on earth with joy for ev - er!

shall be known, His will be done, on earth with joy for ev - er!

shall be known, His will be done, on earth with joy for ev - er!

shall be known, His will be done, on earth with joy for ev - er!

With joy for ev - er!

With joy for ev - er!

With joy for ev - er!

Then round about the starry throne
(From "Samson")

John Milton*
(1608-1674)

Georg Friedrich Händel
(1685-1759)

Edited, and the Organ part arranged, by A.T.D.

* Words selected by N. Hamilton from Milton's "Samson Agonistes".
Copyright, 1936, by E. C. Schirmer Music Co.
For all countries

Published also for Men's Voices (E.C.S. Nº 997)

E. C. S. Nº 1006

heav'n-ly guid-ed soul shall climb,   your heav'n - ly guid-ed soul shall

guid - - ed soul, _ your heav'n-ly guid - - - ed

- ly guid - - ed soul, _ your heav'n-ly guid - - -

mf cresc.

Your heav'n - ly guid - ed soul, _ your heav'n-ly_ guid - -

climb, your heav'n-ly guid - ed soul   shall climb;   Of

soul, _ your heav'n-ly guid-ed soul   shall climb;   Of

- - - - ed soul shall climb;   Of

- - - - ed soul   shall climb;   Of

Ped.

And tri-umph o-ver Death, and

tri-umph o-ver Death, and thee, O Time, and tri - - umph o - ver—

And tri-umph o - ver Death, and

thee, O Time, and thee, O Time, and thee, O Time, and thee,—

Death, and thee, O Time, and thee, O— Time, and

and tri-umph o-ver Death, and thee, O Time, and

Ped.

128

E.C.S. Nº 1006

Thy wisdom, Lord, all thought transcendeth
(Divine Praise: 'Kol Slaven')

Words by H.W.F.

Traditional Russian Melody
Arranged by A.T.D.

E.C.S. № 1007

132

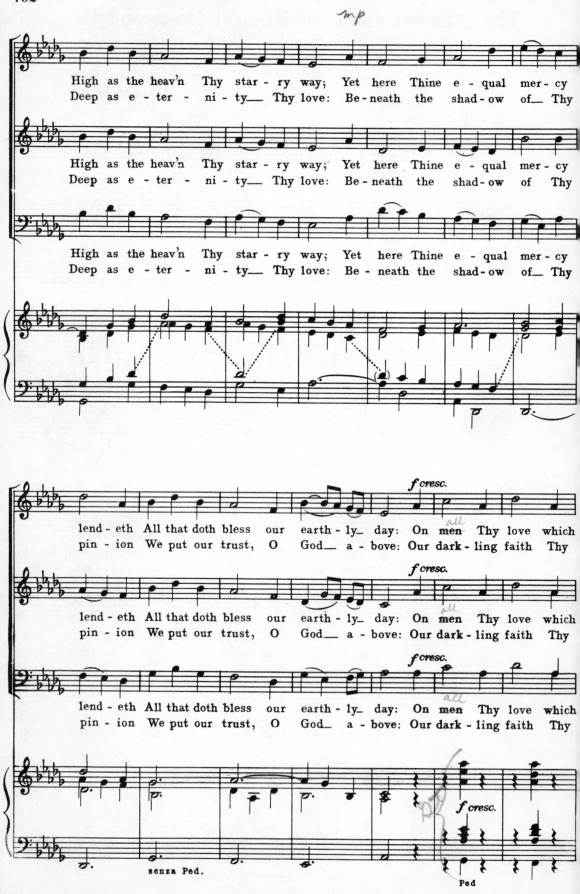

E.C.S. Nº 1007

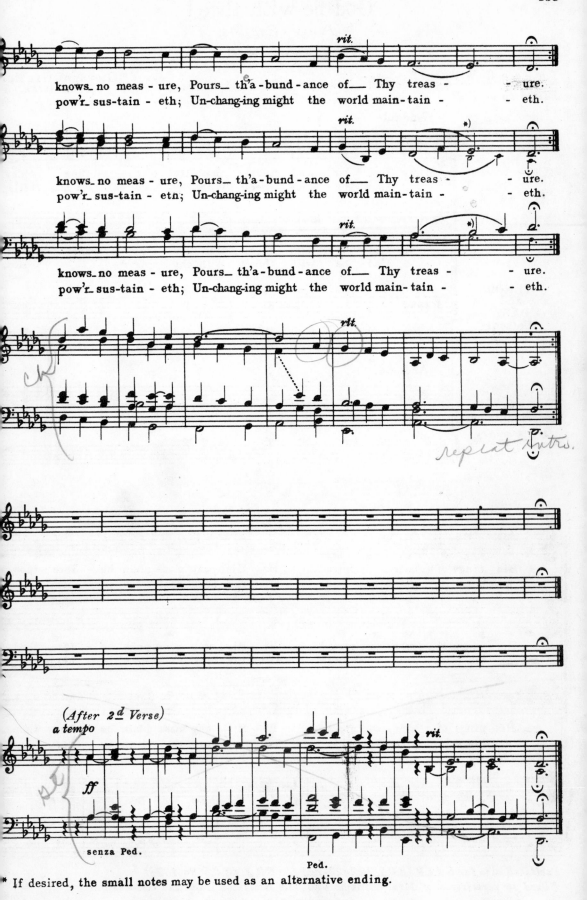

knows— no meas - ure, Pours— th'a-bund-ance of— Thy treas - - ure.
pow'r— sus-tain - eth; Un-chang-ing might the world main-tain - - eth.

knows— no meas - ure, Pours— th'a-bund-ance of— Thy treas - - ure.
pow'r— sus-tain - etn; Un-chang-ing might the world main-tain - - eth.

knows— no meas - ure, Pours— th'a-bund-ance of— Thy treas - - ure.
pow'r— sus-tain - eth; Un-chang-ing might the world main-tain - - eth.

(After 2ᵈ Verse)
a tempo

* If desired, the small notes may be used as an alternative ending.

God be with thee !
(*Pange lingua*)
(*Unaccompanied*)

Theodore C. Williams *
Edited by A.T.D.

Giovanni Grazioli
(1755–1820)

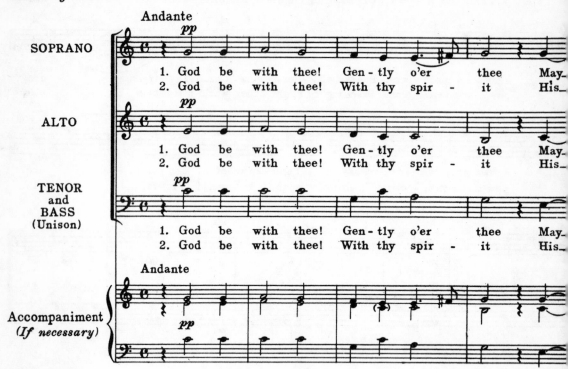

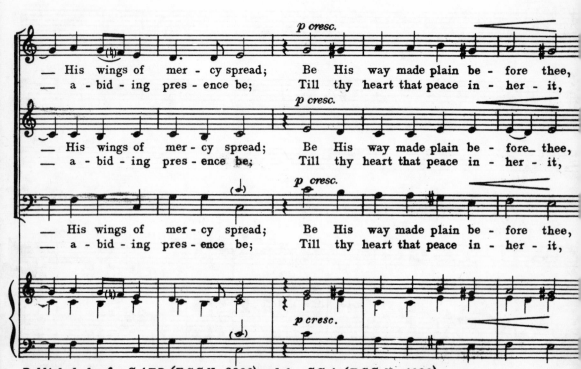

Published also for S.A.T.B. (E.C.S. No. 2223) and for S.S.A. (E.C.S. No. 1928)
Used by permission of Mrs. Williams and The American Unitarian Association.

Copyright, 1936, by E.C. Schirmer Music Co.
For all countries

E.C.S. Nº 1008

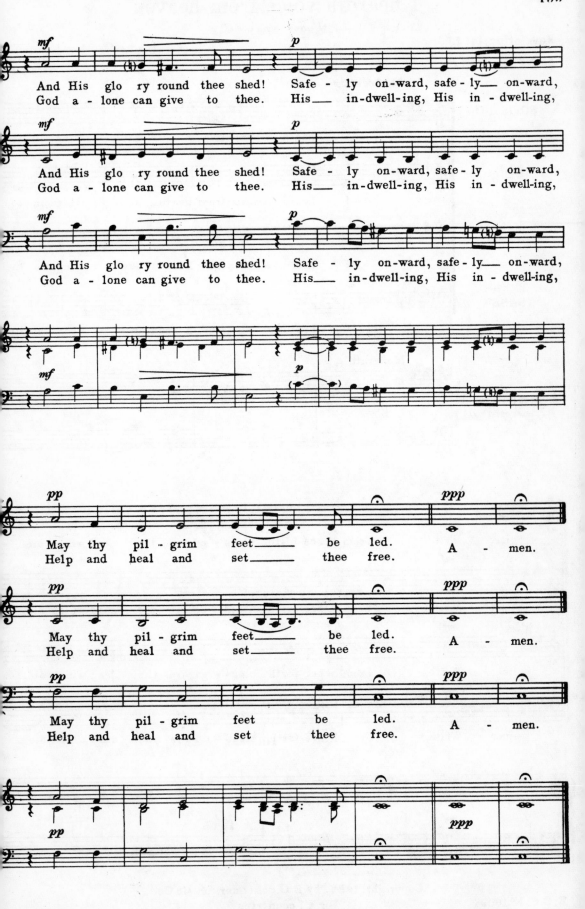

And His glo ry round thee shed! Safe - ly on-ward, safe - ly on-ward,
God a - lone can give to thee. His in-dwell-ing, His in - dwell-ing,

May thy pil - grim feet be led. A - men.
Help and heal and set thee free.

I heard a voice from heaven
(Unaccompanied)

Revelation, 14: 13

Edited by A. T. D.

John Gos
(1800-1880)

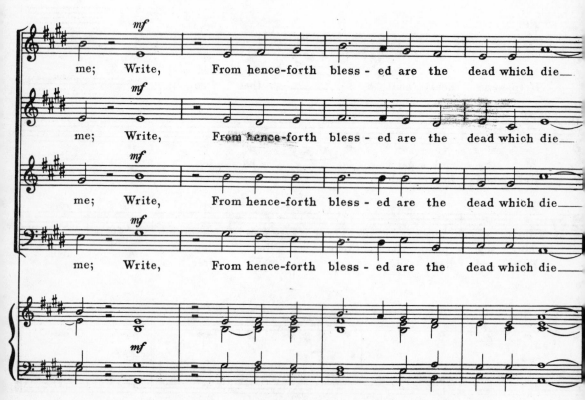

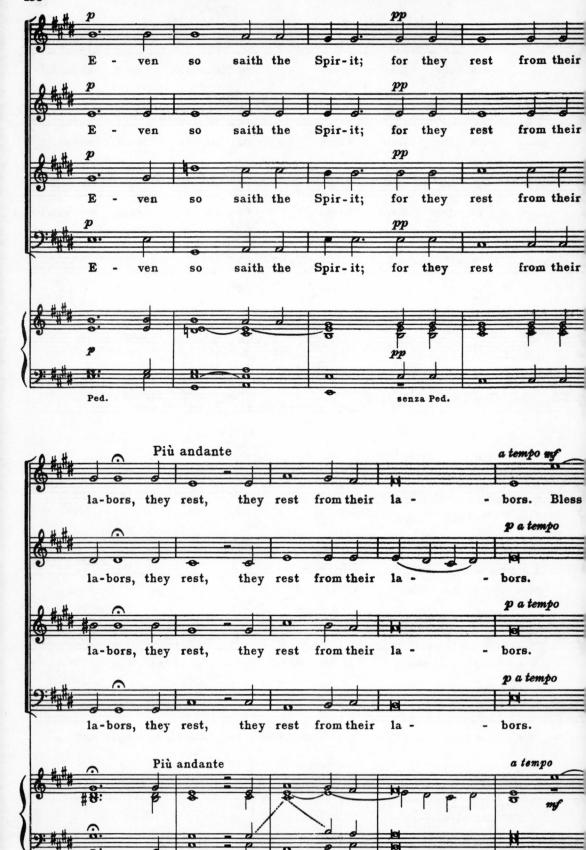

Their bodies are buried in peace

Ecclesiasticus, 44:14

Edited, and the Organ part arranged, by A.T.D.

Georg Friedrich Händel
(1685-1759)

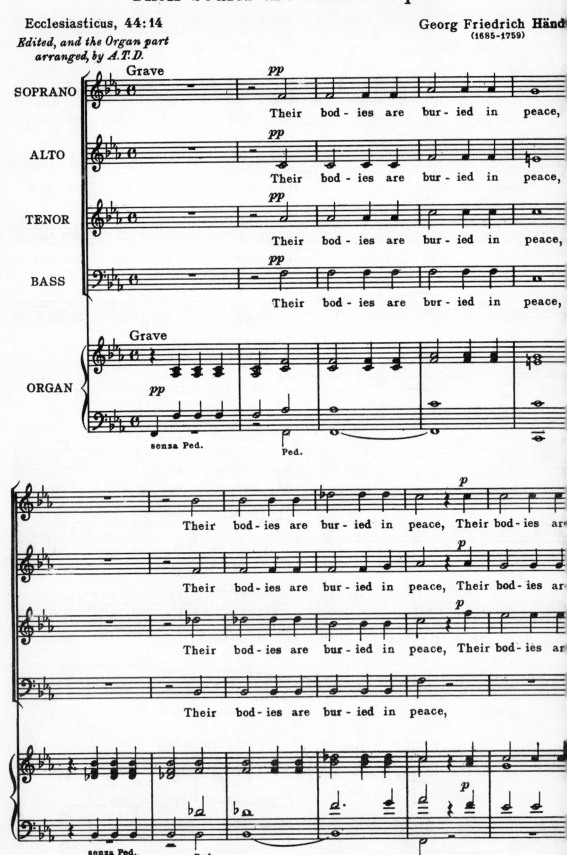

E.C.S. Nº 1010

141

bur - - ied in peace, in

bur - - ied in peace, are bur-ied in

bur - - ied in peace, are bur-ied in

Their bod-ies are bur - ied in

senza Ped.

Ped.

peace,_____ are bur - ied in peace._____

peace,_____ are bur - ied in peace._____

peace,_____ in peace._____

peace._____

E.C.S. No 1010

but their name liv - eth ev - er - more, *mf cresc.* their name,_____

but their name liv - eth ev - er - more, *mf cresc.* their name,_____

but their name liv - eth ev - er - more, their *mf cresc.* name,_____

but their name liv - eth ev - er - more, *mf cresc.* their

mf cresc.

their name,_____ liv - eth

their name,_____ liv - eth

their name,_____ liv - eth

name,_____ liv-eth

ev-er-more,   liv-eth   ev-er-more,

ev-er-more,   liv-eth   ev-er-more,

ev-er-more,   liv-eth   ev-er-more,   thei

ev-er-more,   liv-eth   ev-er-more,   the

Ped.

their name,_____   But the

their name,_____   their name,_____   But the

name,_____   their name,_____   But the

name,_____   But th

senza P

name liv - eth ev - er-more, but their name liv - eth ev - er-more, but their

name liv - eth ev - er-more, but their name liv - eth ev - er-more, but their

name liv - eth ev-er-more, but their name liv - eth ev - er - more, but their

name liv - eth ev - er-more, but their name liv - eth ev - er-more, but their

Ped.

name liv - eth ev - er-more, but their name liv - eth ev - er - more.

name liv - eth ev - er-more, but their name liv - eth ev - er - more.

name liv - eth ev - er-more, but their name liv - eth ev - er - more.

name liv - eth ev - er-more, but their name liv - eth ev - er - more.

All blessed, all holy, Lord God
(Unaccompanied)

Words by H.W.F.

Edited by A.T.D.

Alexander Dimitrievitch Kastalsk[

(1856-   )

light,— Light _____ di - vine; and our_
of light, Thou art the Light _ of _ light,— and our
light,— Light _____ di - vine; and our_
light, Light _____ di - vine;

poco cresc.   mf
eyes_ may_ not_ be-hold_ Thee,— Lord our,_
poco cresc.   mf
eyes_ may_ not be-hold_ Thee, Lord our,_
poco cresc.   mf
eyes_ may not be-hold_ Thee,_ Lord_ our,_

poco cresc.   mf

150

E.C.S. Nº 1011

All people that on earth do dwell
(Unaccompanied)

Psalm 100
Paraphrased by William Kethe (1561)

Thomas Tallis
(1515?-1585)

Edited by A.T.D.

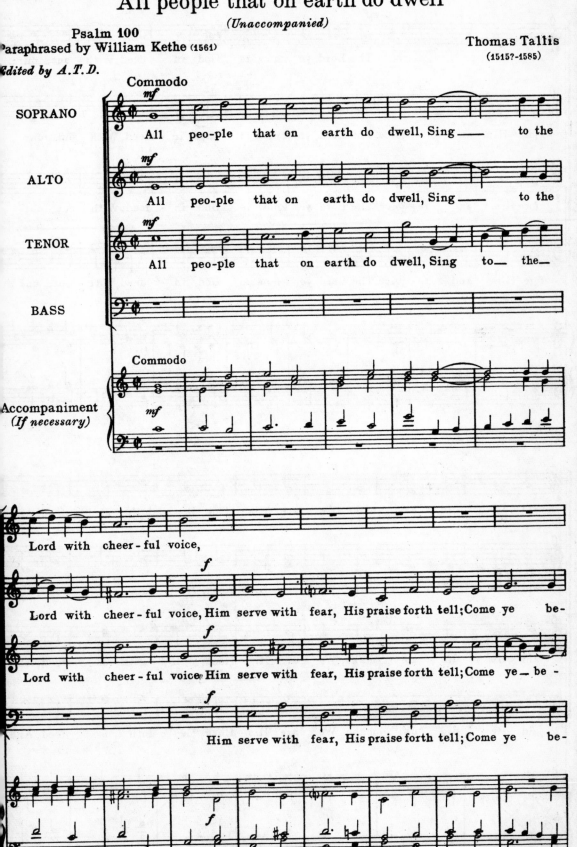

for His sheep He doth us take. O en-ter then His gates with praise, Ap -

for His sheep He doth us take. O en-ter then His gates with praise, Ap -

for His sheep He doth — us take. O en-ter then His gates with praise, Ap -

for His sheep He doth us take.

proach with joy— His— courts un - to;

proach with joy— His— courts un - to; Praise, laud, and bless His name al -

proach with joy His courts un - to; Praise, laud, and bless His name al -

Praise, laud, and bless His name al -

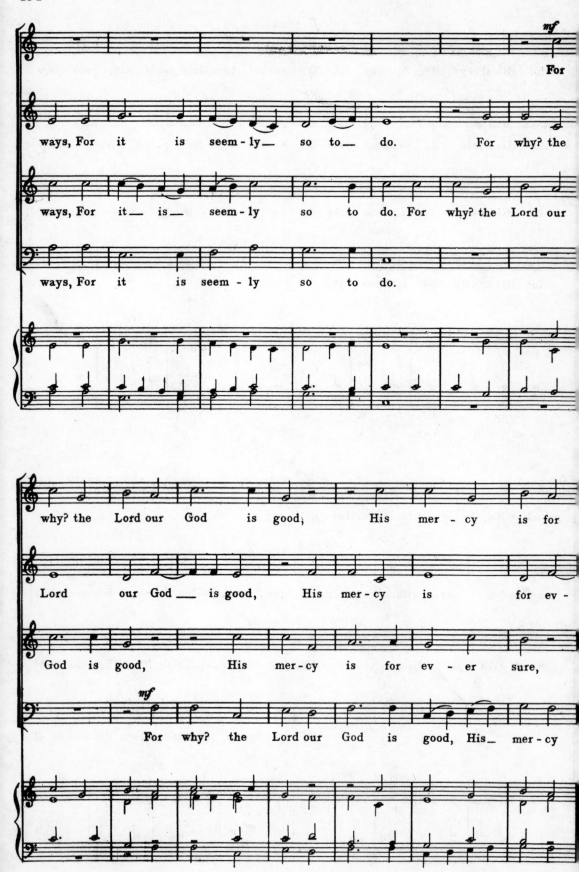

dure, _____ to age en - dure. _____ A - men, _____ a - men,

dure, from age to age en - dure. A - men, a - men, _____ a - men,

dure, from age to age en - dure. A - men, a - men, a - _____ -

dure, from age to age en - dure. A - men, a - men, a - _____ -

a - _____ men, a - _____ men, a - _____ men.

a - _____ - _____ men, a - _____ men.

- _____ men, _____ a - _____ men.

- men, a - _____ men, a - _____ men.

Almighty God, Who hast me brought

(Unaccompanied)

Of unknown authorship
Edited by A. T. D.

Thomas Ford
(1580-1648)

* The sections within brackets may be sung by a small chorus.

C S No 1013

hast me brought In safe-ty to the pres-ent day,

me brought In safe-ty to the pres-ent day, Keep

hast me brought In safe-ty to the pres-ent day, Keep

hast me brought In safe-ty to the pres-ent day,

Keep me from sin in heart and thought, And teach me

me from sin, from sin in heart and thought, And teach me

me from sin in heart and thought, And teach me

Keep me from sin in heart and thought, And teach me

what to do and say, Keep me from sin in

what to do and say, Keep me from sin, from sin in

what to do and say, Keep me from sin _____ in

what to do and say, Keep me from sin in

heart and thought, And teach me what to do and say.

heart and thought, And teach me what to do and say.

heart and thought, And teach me what to do and say.

heart and thought, And teach me what to do and say.

Father of Heaven
(From "Judas Maccabæus")

Thomas Morell
(1703 - 1784)
*Edited, and the Organ part
arranged, by A.T.D.*

Georg Friedrich Händel
(1685-1759)

E.C.S. № 1014

throne, look with an eye of bless - ing down, from Thy e - ter - nal

throne, look with an eye of bless - ing down, from Thy e - ter - nal

throne, look with an eye of bless - ing down, from Thy e - ter - nal

throne, look with an eye of bless - ing down, from Thy e - ter - nal

throne. Fa - ther of Heav'n, from

throne. Fa - ther of Heav'n, from

throne. Fa - ther of Heav'n, from

throne. Fa - ther of Heav'n, from

Thy e-ter-nal throne, from Thy e-
Thy e-ter-nal throne, from Thy e-
Thy e-ter-nal throne, from Thy e-
Thy e-ter-nal throne, from

ter-nal throne, look with an
ter-nal throne, look with an eye of
ter-nal throne, look with an eye of
Thy e-ter-nal throne, look with an

eye   of bless-ing_down, from Thy e - ter - nal_throne,

bless - ing_down,   from Thy   e-ter-nal_throne,

bless - ing_down,   from Thy_e-ter-nal throne,

eye of_bless-ing down,   from Thy e-ter-nal throne,

look_with_an_eye   of_ bless-ing down, from_Thy e - ter - nal_

look_with an   eye   of   bless-ing down, from_Thy e - ter - nal

an_eye of   bless-ing down, from_Thy e - ter - nal

an_eye of   bless-ing down, from Thy e - ter - nal

166

E. C. S. Nº 1014

Grant unto us Thy blessing
(Diffusa est gratia)
(Unaccompanied)

Words by H.W.F.

Edited by A.T.D.

Giovanni Maria Nanini

(circa 1545-1607)

Published also for Men's Voices, — Latin text (E.C.S. Nº949).

in all things   we   may please Thee, O Fa - ther

in all things   we   may   please Thee, O Fa - ther

that   in   all things we may please Thee, may please Thee, O Fa -

that   in   all things we may please   Thee,   O Fa - ther, O

ev - er - last - ing,   For Thou art

ev - er - last - ing,   For Thou art ho -

- ther ev - er - last - ing,   For Thou art ho - ly al - to -

Fa - ther ev - er - last - ing,   For Thou art ho - ly

170

Holy, loving Father
(Dei Mater alma)
(Unaccompanied)

Words by H.W.F.

Edited by A.T.D.

Giovanni Pierluigi da Palestrina

(1526-1594)

173

-drous mer - - cy___ un -

mer - - cy___ un - to Thy

mer - - cy un - - to Thy

Fa - - ther, deep___ Thy mer - cy to

to Thy child - - - - ren's__

child - - ren's child - - - - -

child - ren's child - - - - -

Thy child-ren's child - ren,

C.C.S. Nº 1016

Feb 5, 1989

How lovely is Thy dwelling-place

Psalm 84: 1, 2, 4

Johannes Brahms
(1833-1897)

...ited, and the Organ part
arranged, by A.T.D.

...C.S. Nº 1017

176

E.C.S. Nº 1017

177

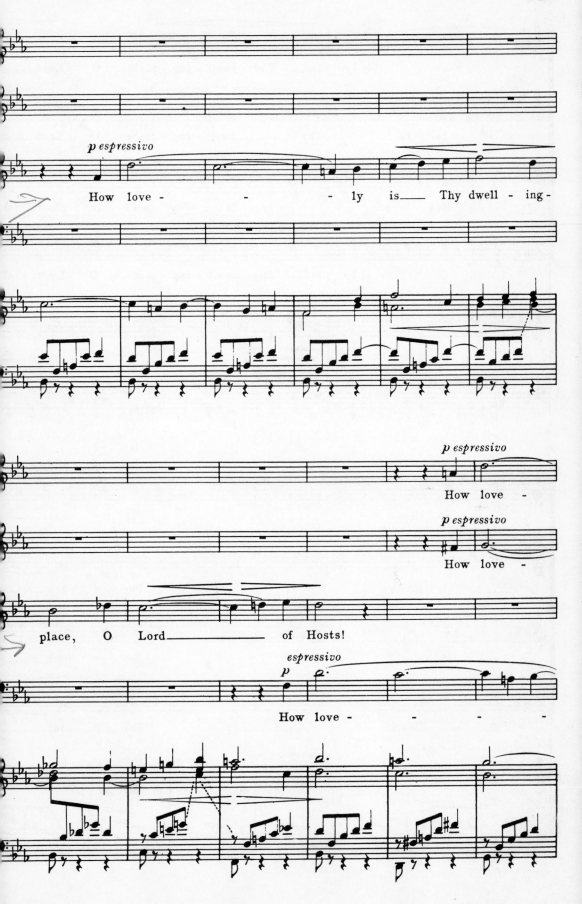

184

186

E.C.S. № 1017

Let Thy merciful ears, O Lord
(Unaccompanied)

From 'The Book of Common Prayer'

Edited by Edmund H. Fellowes *

Thomas Weelkes
(1576?-1623)

**) Moderate speed

SOPRANO

p

Let Thy mer - ci - ful ears, O Lord, be

ALTO

p

Let Thy mer - ci - ful ears, O Lord, be

TENOR

p

Let Thy mer - ci - ful ears, O Lord, be

BASS

p

Let Thy mer - ci - ful ears, O Lord, be

Accompaniment
(*If necessary*)

**) Moderate speed (♩ = about 72)

p

o - pen un - to the prayers of Thy hum - ble ser - - -

o - pen un - to the prayers of Thy hum - ble ser - - -

o - pen un - to the prayers of Thy hum - ble ser - - -

o - pen un - to the prayers of Thy hum - ble ser - - -

* *Reprinted from the* "Tudor Church Music" Series No 37, *by permission of the* Editors *and the* Publisher, the "Oxford University Press".

** Original: a tone lower. The Alto part, missing from the only known set of manuscripts, has been supplied by the Editor.

Lo, my Shepherd's hand divine
(Adapted from the Mass in G-major)

Psalm 23: 1,2
Paraphrased by
James Merrick (1765)
ited, and the Organ part
arranged, by A.T.D.

Franz Josef Haydn
(1732-1809)

Copyright, 1936, by E.C. Schirmer Music Co.
For all countries

C S N° 1019

196

streams that through the ver - dant mead - ows flow.

streams that through the ver - dant mead - ows flow.

streams that through the ver - dant mead - ows flow.

streams that through the ver - dant mead - ows flow.

senza Ped.

pp

p cresc.

dim.

E. C. S. Nº 1019

When I faint_ with sum-mer's heat, He shall lead my wear-y

When I faint_ with sum-mer's heat, He shall lead my wear-y

feet,

He shall lead my wear-y

feet,

He shall lead my wear-y

When I faint_ with sum-mer's heat, He shall lead_ my wear-y

When I faint_ with sum-mer's heat, He shall lead_ my wear-y

198

E.C.S. Nº 1019

To the streams,___ to the streams___ that still_ and slow, Through

To the streams, to the streams, streams that flow Through

To the streams,___ to the streams that still_ and slow, Through

To the streams, to the streams that still and slow, Through

the ver - dant mead - ows flow, still and slow,___

the___ ver - dant mead - ows flow, To the streams___ that

the ver - dant mead - ows flow, To the streams___ that_

the ver - dant mead - ows flow, that_

senza Ped.   Ped.

Mighty Lord, Thy faithfulness abideth ever

(Kyrie eleison)
(Unaccompanied)

Words by H.W.F.

Antonio Lotti
(1667–1740)

Edited by A.T.D.

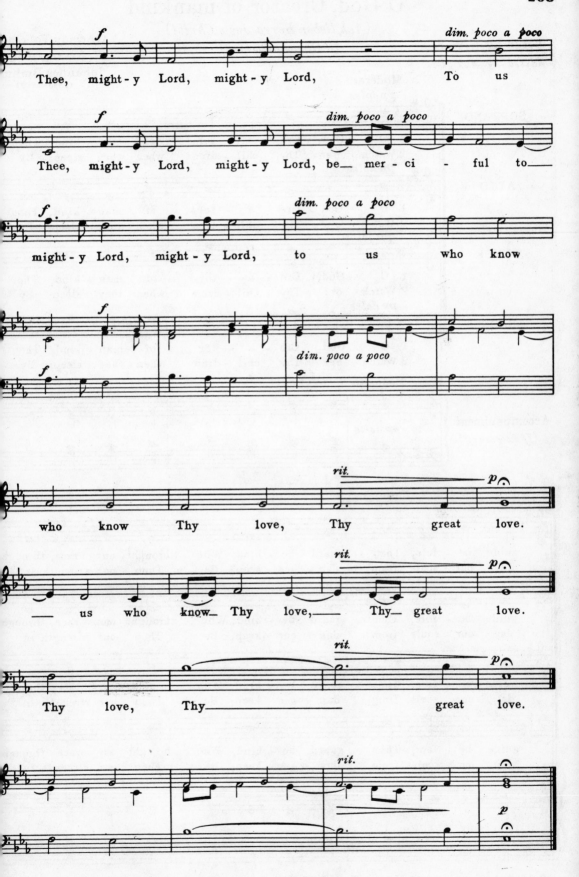

O God, Creator of mankind
(Ach lieber Herre Jesu Christ)
(Unaccompanied)

Words by H.W.F.
Edited by A.T.D.

German Folk-so
Arranged by
Johannes Brahm
(1833-1897)

Published also for Men's Voices (E. C. S. Nº921).

p

years un - told, From long - for - got - ten days of old; Thy
work be - gun, Be Thou our rest in la - bor done; Thy

chil-dren guide _____ to - day, And guard us when _____ we stray!
chil-dren guard _____ to - day, Be Thou our guide, _____ we pray!

pp *rit. e dim.*

rit. *pp* *dim.*

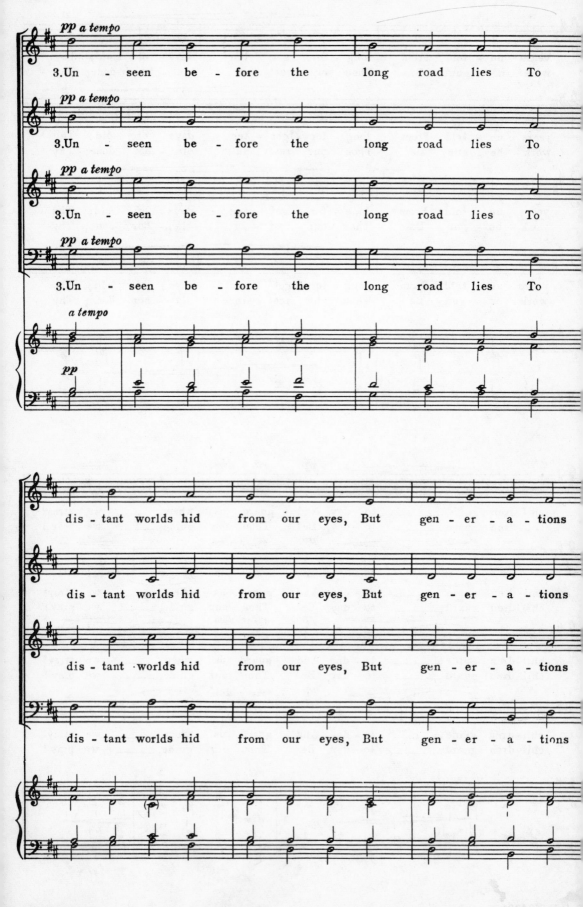

yet un-born Shall lift their brows to greet the morn, To

yet un-born Shall lift their brows to greet the morn, To

yet un-born Shall lift their brows to greet the morn, To

yet un-born Shall lift their brows to greet the morn, To

Thee in faith shall pray, Thy chil-dren guide to-day!

Thee in faith shall pray, Thy chil-dren guide to-day!

Thee in faith shall pray, Thy chil-dren guide to-day!

Thee in faith shall pray, Thy chil-dren guide to-day!

O Lord, give Thy Holy Spirit

(Unaccompanied)

Edited by A.T.D.

Thomas Tal[...]
(1515?-1585)

dwell in the fear of Thy Name, in the fear of

dwell in the fear of Thy Name, in the fear of Thy Name, in the

that we may dwell in the fear of Thy Name, in the

that we may dwell in the fear of Thy Name, in the fear

Thy Name, all the days of our life,

fear of Thy Name all the days of our life all

fear of Thy Name, in the fear of The Name, all

of Thy Name, in the fear of Thy Name, all the days

210

E.C.S. No 1022

sent, and Je-sus Christ whom Thou___ hast___ sent, and

sent, and Je - sus Christ whom Thou___ hast sent,

Thou hast sent, and Je - sus Christ whom Thou___ hast sent, and

sent, and Je - sus Christ whom Thou hast sent, and

Je - - sus Christ whom Thou hast sent.

and Je - sus Christ whom Thou hast___ sent.

Je - sus Christ whom Thou___ hast___ sent.

Je - sus Christ whom Thou___ hast sent.

O Saviour of the world
[O Lord of all mankind]
(*Unaccompanied*)

From 'The Book of Common Prayer'
Alternative words adapted by H.W.F.

John Gos
(1800-1880)

Edited by A.T.D.

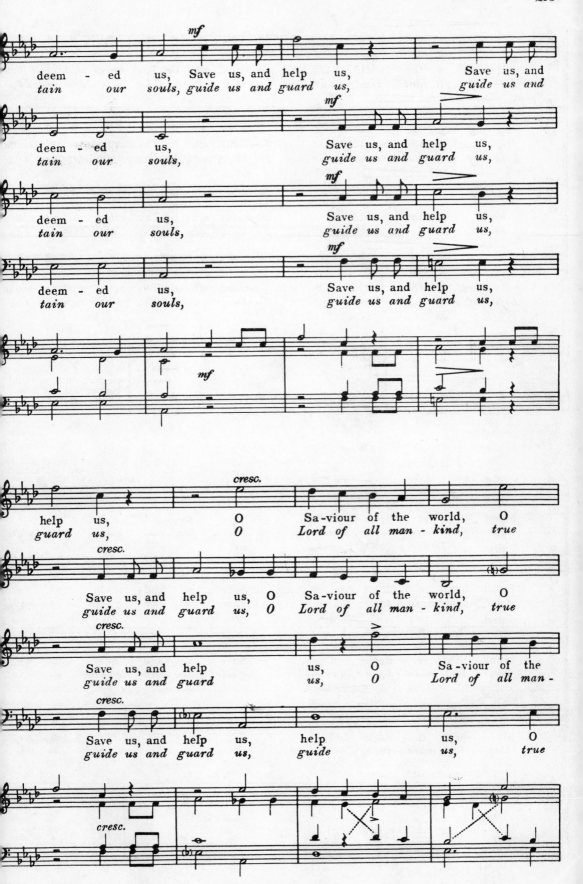

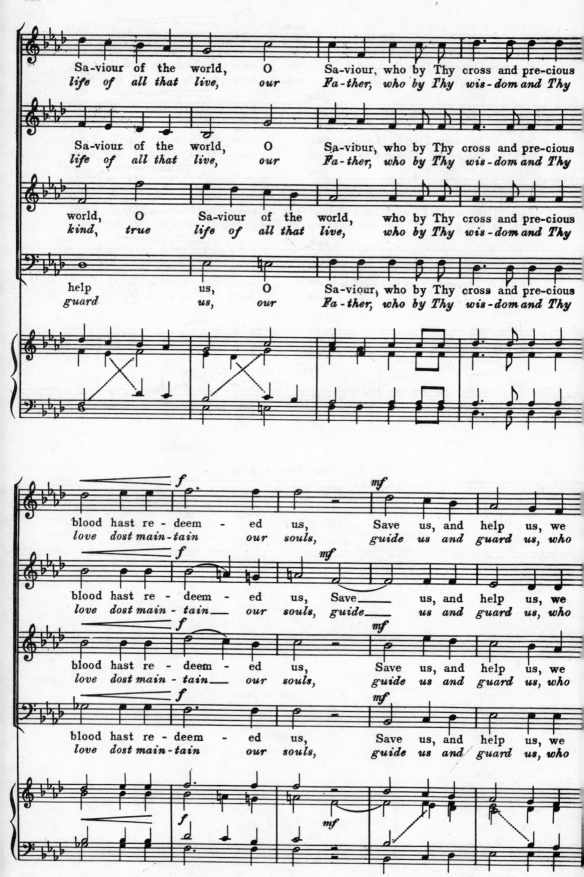

Thou Life of life
(Unaccompanied)

Words by H.W.F.

Edited by A.T.D.

Paul Tchesnokov

(1877-)

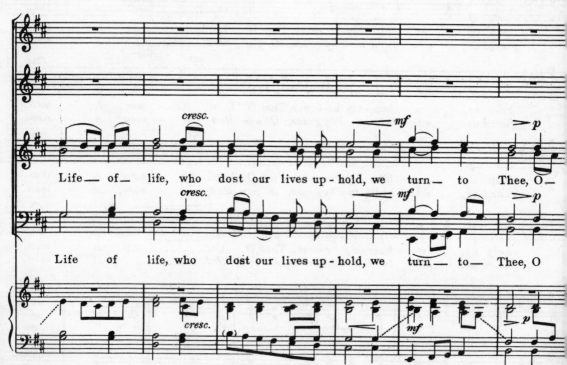

E.C.S. Nº 1024

220

E.C.S. No 1024

for— we are— Thy chil - dren, yea, we rest —— in Thee,

for we are Thy chil - dren, yea, we rest —— in Thee, —

we are Thy chil-dren, we are— Thy chil-dren, yea, we rest in Thee,—

we are Thy chil-dren, are Thy chil - dren, yea, we rest in Thee,—

yea, we rest in Thee. ——

yea, we rest in Thee, — yea, we rest in Thee.

yea, we rest in Thee, — yea, we rest— in Thee. ——

yea, we rest— in Thee, —— yea, we rest— in Thee.

Turn Thee, again, O Lord

Psalm 90: 13

Edited by A.T.D.

Thomas Attwood
(1765 – 1838)

SOPRANO: Turn Thee, a-gain, O Lord, ___ at the last, turn Thee, turn Thee, O Lord, ___ at ___ the last, ___ and be gra-cious, be gra-cious un-to Thy

ALTO: Turn Thee, a-gain, O Lord, at the last, turn Thee, turn Thee, O Lord, at the last, be gra-cious un -

TENOR: Turn Thee, a-gain, O Lord, at the last, turn Thee, turn Thee, O Lord, at the last, ___ and be gra-cious un-to Thy ser - -

BASS: Turn Thee, a-gain, O Lord, at the last, O Lord, at the last, and be gra-cious un - to Thy

SEMI-CHORUS

Turn Thee, a - gain, O Lord,— at— the last; turn Thee,

Turn Thee, a - gain, O Lord,— at— the last; turn Thee,

Turn Thee, a - gain, O Lord, at the last; turn Thee, turn Thee,

Turn Thee, a - gain, O Lord, at the last; turn Thee,

senza Ped.

p
vants, be gra-cious, be gra-cious un-to Thy ser - - vants.
p
vants, be gra-cious, un - to Thy ser - - vants.
p
vants, be gra-cious, un - to Thy ser - - vants.
p
vants, be gra-cious, un - to Thy ser - - vants.
p
FULL CHORUS
pp
Turn Thee, a-gain, O Lord, at the last, turn Thee, turn Thee, O
pp
Turn Thee, a-gain, O Lord, at the last, turn Thee, turn Thee, O
pp
Turn Thee, a-gain, O Lord, at the last, turn Thee, turn Thee, O
pp
Turn Thee, a-gain, O Lord, at the last, O
pp
senza Ped.
Ped.

226

We walk the earth as pilgrims

(Ich bin ein Gast auf Erden)

(Unaccompanied)

Words by H. W. F.

Edited by A. T. D.

Bartholomäus Gesiu
(1560-1613)

a bright - - er strand. Here all our days we la - -
tal breathe in dream. God laid the deep found-a - -

a bright - er strand. Here all our days we la -
tal breathe in dream. God laid the deep found-a -

a bright - er strand. Here all our days we la -
- tal breathe in dream. God laid the deep found - a -

a bright - er strand. Here all our days we la -
- tal breathe in dream. God laid the deep found - a -

bor In wear - i - ness and pain; There waits a bet - ter
tions, He hath pre - par'd the plan; He sum - mon - eth the

bor In wear - i - ness and pain; There waits a bet - ter
tions, He hath pre - par'd the plan; He sum - mon - eth the

bor In wear - i - ness and pain; There waits a bet - ter
tions, He hath pre - par'd the plan; He sum - mon - eth the

bor In wear - i - ness and pain; There waits a bet - ter
tions, He hath pre - par'd the plan; He sum - mon - eth the

230

E.C.S. Nº 1026

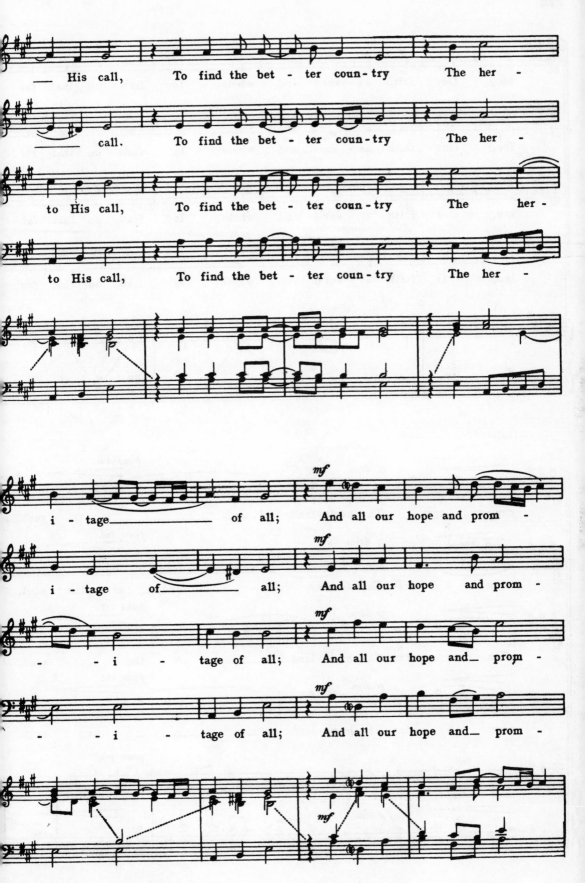

INDEX OF FIRST LINES

MIXED VOICES

THE CONCORD ANTHEM BOOK (*Concord Series No. 13*) 40 Anthems for Mixed Voices, *compiled by* Davison and Foote   Cloth $2.75

THE SECOND CONCORD ANTHEM BOOK (*Concord Series No. 1200*) 40 Anthems for Mixed Voices, *compiled by* Davison and Foote   Cloth $2.75

THIRD CONCORD ANTHEM BOOK (*Concord Series No. 1290*) 30 Anthems for Mixed Voices, *compiled by* Victoria Glaser. *Edited by* Henry Clough-Leighter   Cloth $2.75

LITURGICAL RESPONSES (*No. 2279*) 26 Individual Responses for Mixed Voices, *by* Matthew Lundquist   Paper $1.25

THE GATEWAY (*No. 1792*) 20 Anthems for Soprano, Alto and Baritone, *Edited by* Matthew Lundquist   Paper $1.50

BACH CHORALS — Book I (*Concord Series No. 1*) 25 Chorals for Unison or Mixed Voices (Adult or Junior Choirs)   Cloth $2.00
                                                                          Paper $1.25

Instrumental parts for Quartet of Strings now available. (Violin I, II, Viola, and Violoncello) A Violin III has also been included for use when a Viola player is not available.
                                    each part $ .65

BACH CHORALS — Book II (*Concord Series No. 615*) 28 Chorals for Unison or Mixed Voices (Adult or Junior Choirs)   Cloth $2.00
                                                                          Paper $1.25

BACH CHORALS — Book III (*Concord Series No. 1799*) 25 Chorals for Unison or Mixed Voices (Adult or Junior Choirs)   Cloth $2.00
                                                                          Paper $1.25

WOMEN'S VOICES

BACH CHORALS — Book IV (*Vassar Series No. 875*) 27 Chorals for Women's Voices (Four-part)   Cloth $2.00
                                                                          Paper $1.25

BACH CHORALS — Book V (*Vassar Series No. 878*) 26 Chorals for Women's Voices (Three-part)   Cloth $2.00
                                                                          Paper $1.25

THE GREEN HILL Three-part Sacred Music for Women's Voices (*No. 1838*) 38 Anthems for Soprano I & II and Alto   Paper $2.50

JUNIOR CHOIR

FAIR HAVEN Junior Choir and Duet Book (*Commonwealth Series No. 1957*) 27 Anthems for Soprano and Alto   Paper $1.75

GREEN HILL Junior Choir and Duet Book (*Commonwealth Series No. 1546*) 35 Anthems for Soprano and Alto   Paper $2.00

CONCORD HYMNAL (*Concord Series No. 10*) for Day School, Sunday School and Home   Board $1.50

SELECTED HYMNS 46 Standard Hymns for use in School and Home (*Words and melodies only*)   Paper   .65

THE LITTLE CHURCH Choir Book (*No. 1984*) 30 Anthems (Unison and Two-part) for Junior Choir, *compiled by* Matthew N. Lundquist
                                                                                    $1.50

ANTHOLOGY

PROTESTANT CHURCH MUSIC IN AMERICA *by* Archibald T. Davison
                                                                                    3.00

Sacred Music

MIXED VOICES
FOUR PARTS UNLESS OTHERWISE INDICATED
(GROUP 11)

2289	Ave verum Corpus (Motet) L. & E. (S.& A.,T.B.)	C. Franco	.18
2290	Tantum ergo (Motet) L. & E. (S.& A.,T B.)	C. Franco	.18
2291	O salutaris hostia (Motet) L. & E.	Pietro Müller	.18
2292	Pie Jesu (S.S.B.) Score, chorus & inst. parts, complete	Marc-A. Charpentier	2.50
2293	A Program of Six Chorals	Johann Sebastian Bach	.20
2294	The Last Words of David	Randall Thompson	.30
2297	Pat-a-pan (S.A.B.)	Burgundian Air	.20
2298	En natus est Emanuel (Born is the Lord Emanuel)	Michael Praetorius	.18
2400	Christe, quum sit jam exire (Christ, now at Thy Passion)	Emanuele d'Astorga	.35
2401	O sacred head, now wounded	Johann Sebastian Bach	.18
2402	Who trusts in God, a strong abode	Matthew N. Lundquist	.30
2403	Now let every tongue adore Thee (S.A.B.)	Johann Sebastian Bach	.16
2405	To God on high be thanks and praise (S.A.B.)	Nikolaus Decius	.12
2406	If ye love Me, keep My commandments (S.A.B.)	Thomas Tallis	.16
2407	Song of the bagpipers (I. & E.)	Italian Carol	.18
2408	Song of the bagpipers (S.A.B. or S.A.T.) E.	Italian Carol	.16
1290	Third Concord Anthem Book (30 Anthems) Victoria Glaser & H. Clough-Leighter		2.50
2409	Friede auf Erden (Peace on Earth) G. & E.	Arnold Schönberg	
2410	Christmas Day is coming (Arr. Ruth Abbott)	Irish Carol	.18
2411	Wassail Bough, The (Arr. Ruth Abbott)	English Carol	.40
2412	Twelve days of Christmas, The (Arr. Ruth Abbott)	English Carol	.50
2413	You may bury me in the East (Contralto solo)	John W. Work	.20
2414	Lacrymosa (Day of Sadness) L. & E. (Requiem) Piano	Wolfgang A. Mozart	.18
2420	Magnificat (Piano or String Orchestra)	John Crawford	.75
2421	Ave Maria (Hail, Virgin Mary) L. & E.	Sherwood M. Shäffer	.25
2422	Mother's Hymn, The (Anthem for Mother's Day)	Matthew N. Lundquist	.22
2423	Ah! Gabriel (S.A.B.) Piano (Arr. V.G.)	Italian Carol	.18
2424	Thy Light is come (Christmas Anthem) Organ	Henry Clough-Leighter	.25
2425	Praise the Lord (Unison and Four-part) Solo voice (Organ)	Richard Stark	.25
2426	Mass of the Holy Spirit (Communion Service)	Randall Thompson	2.00
2427	Holy, Holy, Holy (Heilig, heilig, heilig) G. & E. (Organ) Edited Mattfeld	Franz Peter Schubert	.20
2430	Ave Regina Caelorum (O most blessed Spirit) L. & E. (S.S.A.T.B.)	Frank H. Smith	.20
2431	Look down, O Lord	William Byrd	
2432	Christmas Story, The (Die Weihnachtsgeschichte)	Hugo Distler	

E. C. SCHIRMER MUSIC CO.

221 Columbus Avenue   Boston, Mass.

Sacred Music

MIXED VOICES
FOUR PARTS UNLESS OTHERWISE INDICATED
(GROUP 12)

No.	Title	Composer	Price
2434	A star is moving (Arr. M.N.L.)	Mediaeval Carol	.18
2435	Lift up your heads (Arr. M.N.L.)	Melchior Vulpius	.18
2436	Now praise we Christ (Arr. M.N.L.)	5th Century Plain Song	.18
2437	Star in the East (Christmas Anthem)	Howard Boatwright	.35
2438	Creator of the stars (Advent Hymn)	Howard Boatwright	.30
2439	Nunc sancte nobis Spiritus (Come, Holy Spirit) L. & E.	Howard Boatwright	**28**
2440	Hear my cry, O God (Psalm 61)	Howard Boatwright	.25
2441	God is our refuge (Psalm 46)	Howard Boatwright	.20
2444	Whoso loveth me (Edited Mattfeld)	Melchoir Vulpius	
2445	O how great and glorious (Edited Mattfeld)	Jakob Vaet	
2446	Short Communion Service in C (Optional Organ)	John Davison	
2447	Now God be praised (S.A.B.) Arr. V.G.	Melchior Vulpius	.18
2448	Ego ipse consolabor vos (I am He that comforteth you) L. & E.	Frank H. Smith	
2449	Adoramus te, Christe (We adore Thee, O Lord Christ) L. & E. (Organ)	Ludovico da Viadana	
2450	Now come, Thou Savior of men (Nun komm, der Heiden Heiland) G. & E. (S.S.T.) Organ	Johann Hermann Schein	
2451	Now blessed be Thou, Christ Jesu (Gelobet seist du, Jesu Christ) G. & E. (S.S.T. or S.A.B.) Organ	Johann Hermann Schein	
2452	Ye children who do praise the Lord	Scottish Psalter	
2453	Agnus Dei (Lamb of God) L. & E. (Piano)	Franz Josef Haydn	
2454	Morning Hymn	Howard Boatwright	.35
2455	Touro-louro-louro!	French Carol	
2456	Daughter Zion, now rejoice! (S.A.B.) Arr. M.N.L.	Georg Friedrich Handel	.18
2457	For Thou art worthy to be praised (S.A.B.) Arr. V.G.	Piotr Tchaikovsky	
2458	Praise to God, who rules the earth (S.A.B.) Organ (Arr. V.G.)	Georg Friedrich Handel	
2459	Requiem (Double-Chorus)	Randall Thompson	2.25
2463	Kyrie (Mass of the Holy Spirit) L.	Randall Thompson	.30
2464	Gloria (Mass of the Holy Spirit) E.	Randall Thompson	.35
2465	Credo (Mass of the Holy Spirit) E.	Randall Thompson	.35
2466	Sanctus (Mass of the Holy Spirit) E.	Randall Thompson	.45
2467	Benedictus (Mass of the Holy Spirit) E.	Randall Thompson	.25
2468	Hosanna (Mass of the Holy Spirit) E.	Randall Thompson	.20
2469	Agnus Dei (Mass of the Holy Spirit) E.	Randall Thompson	.25

E. C. SCHIRMER MUSIC CO.
221 Columbus Avenue   Boston, Mass.